Piano
Scales & Arpeggios

for Trinity Guildhall examinations
from 2007

Initial–Grade 5

Published by:
Trinity College London
89 Albert Embankment
London SE1 7TP UK

T +44 (0)20 7820 6100
F +44 (0)20 7820 6161
E music@trinityguildhall.co.uk
www.trinityguildhall.co.uk

Printed in England by Halstan & Co. Ltd, Amersham, Bucks.

The fingering given in this book is offered as a recommendation only. Any other logical system of fingering is acceptable provided that it is consistent and allows an even execution of the requirements.

Please note that the recommended speeds are a guide to what can be expected at each level. For the purposes of fulfilling examination criteria, accuracy, fluency and evenness of touch and tone should be regarded as equally important aspects of technical competence.

One example of a *legato* and *staccato* scale and arpeggio has been given for reference at the start of each relevant grade. Candidates should note that both *legato* and *staccato* versions of **every** scale and arpeggio should be prepared where required by the syllabus currently in force.

Initial

The following scales to be performed hands separately, ♩ = 60, *legato* and *mf*:

C major (one octave)

A minor (one octave): candidate's choice of *either* harmonic *or* melodic *or* natural minor

Candidates must also play Exercises − see *Piano Initial Pieces and Exercises* album.

C major (one octave)

Right hand

Left hand

A minor: harmonic (one octave)

Right hand

Left hand

Initial continued

A minor: melodic (one octave)

Right hand

Left hand

A minor: natural (one octave)

Right hand

Left hand

Grade 1

Scales and broken chords

The following scales, ♩ = 70, and broken chords, ♩. = 50, to be performed hands separately, *legato* and *mf*:

F and G major (one octave)

D and E minor (one octave): candidate's choice of *either* harmonic *or* melodic *or* natural minor scale

Chromatic scale in contrary motion, hands together, starting on D (one octave)

Candidates must also play Exercises – see *Piano Grade 1 Pieces and Exercises* album.

F major scale (one octave)

Right hand

Left hand

F major broken chord (one octave)

Right hand

Left hand

Grade 1 continued

G major scale (one octave)

Right hand

Left hand

G major broken chord (one octave)

Right hand

Left hand

D minor scale: harmonic (one octave)

Right hand

Left hand

D minor scale: melodic (one octave)

Right hand

Left hand

D minor scale: natural (one octave)

Right hand

Left hand

D minor broken chord (one octave)

Right hand

Left hand

Grade 1 continued

E minor scale: harmonic (one octave)

Right hand

Left hand

E minor scale: melodic (one octave)

Right hand

Left hand

E minor scale: natural (one octave)

Right hand

Left hand

E minor broken chord (one octave)

Right hand

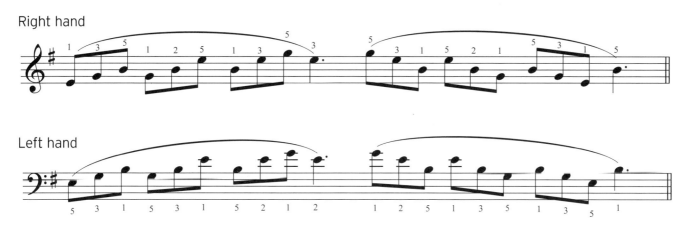

Left hand

Chromatic scale in contrary motion hands together, starting on D (one octave)

Grade 2

i) Scales

The following scales to be performed hands together, ♩ = 80 and *legato*, **f** or **p** as requested by the examiner:

Bb and D major (two octaves)

G and B minor (two octaves): candidate's choice of *either* harmonic *or* melodic minor

Chromatic scale similar motion starting on Bb (two octaves)

ii) Arpeggios

The following arpeggios to be performed hands separately, ♩ = 60, *legato* and **mf**:

Bb and D major (two octaves)

G and B minor (two octaves)

Candidates must also play Exercises − see *Piano Grade 2 Pieces and Exercises* album.

Bb major scale (two octaves)

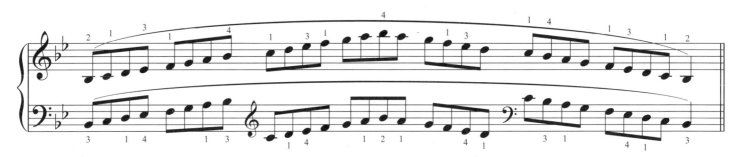

Bb major arpeggio (two octaves)

Right hand

Left hand

D major scale (two octaves)

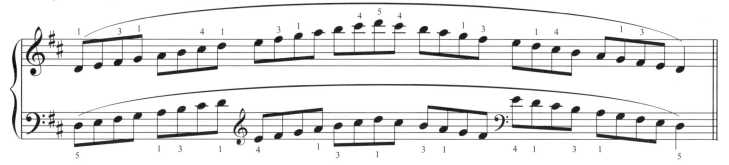

D major arpeggio (two octaves)

Right hand

Left hand

G minor scale: harmonic (two octaves)

G minor scale: melodic (two octaves)

Grade 2 continued

G minor arpeggio (two octaves)

Right hand

Left hand

B minor scale: harmonic (two octaves)

B minor scale: melodic (two octaves)

B minor arpeggio (two octaves)

Right hand

Left hand

Chromatic scale in similar motion starting on B♭ (two octaves)

Grade 3

i) Scales

The following scales to be performed hands together, ♩ = 90 and *legato*, 𝒇 or 𝒑 as requested by the examiner:

Eb and A major (two octaves)

C and F# minor (two octaves): candidate's choice of *either* harmonic *or* melodic minor

Eb major contrary motion scale (two octaves)

ii) Arpeggios

The following arpeggios to be performed hands separately, ♩ = 70, *legato* and *mf*:

Eb and A major (two octaves)

C and F# minor (two octaves)

Candidates must also play Exercises – see *Piano Grade 3 Pieces and Exercises* album.

Eb major scale (two octaves)

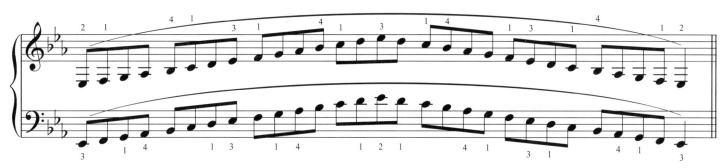

Eb major arpeggio (two octaves)

Right hand

Left hand

A major scale (two octaves)

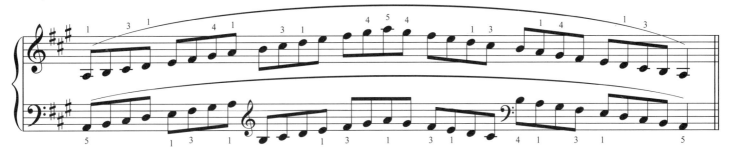

A major arpeggio (two octaves)

Right hand

Left hand

C minor scale: harmonic (two octaves)

C minor scale: melodic (two octaves)

Grade 3 continued

C minor arpeggio (two octaves)

Right hand

Left hand

F# minor scale: harmonic (two octaves)

F# minor scale: melodic (two octaves)

F# minor arpeggio (two octaves)

Right hand

Left hand

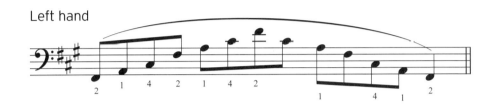

E♭ major contrary motion scale (two octaves)

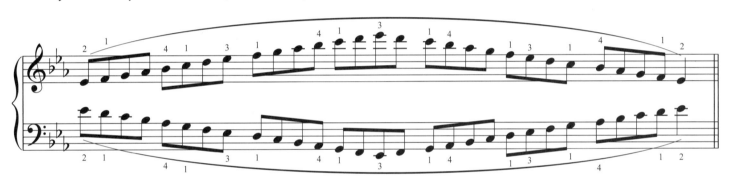

Grade 4

i) Scales

The following scales to be performed hands together, ♩ = 100, *legato* or *staccato* (as given in the first example), *f* or *p* as requested by the examiner:

A♭ and E major (two octaves)

F and C♯ minor (two octaves): candidate's choice of *either* harmonic *or* melodic minor

A♭ major contrary motion scale (two octaves)

Chromatic scale in similar motion starting on A♭, C, E and F (two octaves)

ii) Arpeggios

The following arpeggios to be performed hands separately, ♩ = 80, *legato*, *f* or *p* as requested by the examiner:

A♭ and E major (two octaves)

F and C♯ minor (two octaves)

Candidates must also play Exercises – see *Piano Grade 4 Pieces and Exercises* album.

A♭ major scale (two octaves), *legato*

A♭ major scale (two octaves), *staccato*

A♭ major arpeggio (two octaves)

Right hand

Left hand

E major scale (two octaves)

E major arpeggio (two octaves)

Right hand

Left hand

F minor scale: harmonic (two octaves)

Grade 4 continued

F minor scale: melodic (two octaves)

F minor arpeggio (two octaves)

Right hand

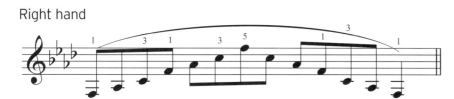

Left hand

C# minor scale: harmonic (two octaves)

C# minor scale: melodic (two octaves)

20

C♯ minor arpeggio (two octaves)

Right hand

Left hand

A♭ major scale: contrary motion (two octaves)

Chromatic scale: similar motion starting on A♭, C, E, F (two octaves), for example:

Grade 5

i) Scales

The following scales to be performed hands together, ♩ = 110, *legato* or *staccato* (as given in the first example), $\boldsymbol{f}$ or $\boldsymbol{p}$ as requested by the examiner:

D♭ and B major (two octaves)

B♭ and G♯ minor (two octaves): candidate's choice of *either* harmonic *or* melodic minor

G harmonic minor contrary motion scale (two octaves)

ii) Arpeggios

The following arpeggios to be performed hands together, ♩ = 90, *legato* or *staccato* (as given in the first example), $\boldsymbol{f}$ or $\boldsymbol{p}$ as requested by the examiner:

D♭ and B major (two octaves)

B♭ and G♯ minor (two octaves)

Diminished 7th starting on B (two octaves)

Candidates must also play Exercises − see *Piano Grade 5 Pieces and Exercises* album.

D♭ major scale, *legato*

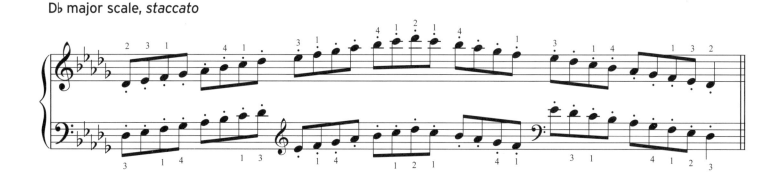

D♭ major scale, *staccato*

Db major arpeggio (two octaves)

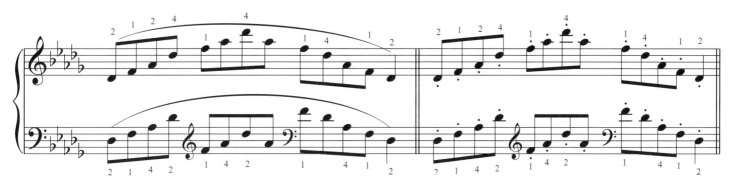

B major scale (two octaves)

B major arpeggio (two octaves)

Bb minor scale: harmonic (two octaves)

Grade 5 continued

B♭ minor scale: melodic (two octaves)

B♭ minor arpeggio (two octaves)

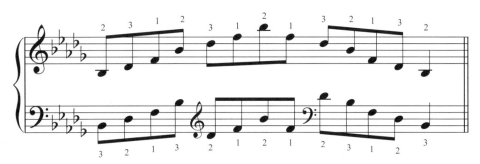

G♯ minor scale: harmonic (two octaves)

G♯ minor scale: melodic (two octaves)

G# minor arpeggio (two octaves)

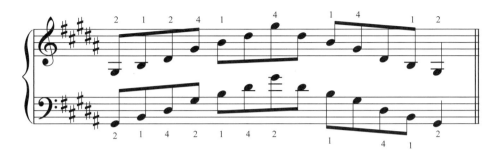

G minor scale: harmonic, contrary motion (two octaves)

Diminished 7th starting on B (two octaves)

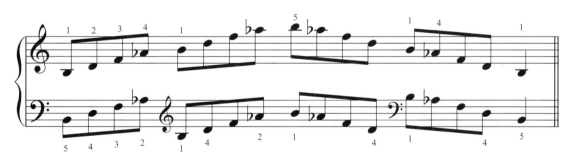